D1060382

This book is dedicated to Wolfie,
who struggles to slow down and focus but
is getting better and better, each and every day.

Slow Down, Alfie!

Written by Sara Moore & Christopher Piehler

Illustrated by Sara Moore

Presented by

Silver Lining Stuffies®

Alfie LOVED to run around
the forest playing with friends.
They called themselves the "Woodsy Willy Sillies."

Alfie was really fast and really strong.
Alfie loved playing basketball and
karate with the Sillies.

But sometimes, the Sillies got frustrated when Alfie didn't slow down for them...

Alfie, we're pooped!!!

Chase me!

3

...or when Alfie played basketball
AND karate at the same time.

They were worried.

Just slow down, Alfie!
You're too fast!

But Alfie wasn't listening.
Alfie couldn't sit still, and was distracted by every
bird and butterfly that flapped by.

When Alfie got home, focusing on woodland chores was really hard.

Alfie, you're supposed to be cleaning up the den!

Karate doesn't work on birds, silly!

Alfie, you're supposed to be gathering food!

Alfie's Mom and Dad were worried.

Why can't Alfie stay focused on tasks?

WOLF OF
WALL STREET

Maybe we can use mindfulness to
teach Alfie how to relax and focus
on one thing at a time.

What's mindfulness?

I'll show you.

Alfie and Mom and Dad
sat under a tree together.

Close your eyes and
describe what you're
smelling and hearing and
feeling on your fur.

Can't I go play
basketball instead?

Not right now. Just
focus on being here.

So Alfie sat still and sniffed.
Alfie could smell the pine trees
and feel a breeze blowing by.

Together, they helped Alfie focus on his
breathing and picture playing with friends calmly,
one sport at a time.

The next day, the Sillies went to play.
Alfie was super excited, and tried to play karate
and basketball at the same time.

Alfie, this is basketball.
You can't CHOP!

But Alfie stopped. And breathed. And slowed down.
And they had so much fun, playing basketball,
THEN trying out new karate moves.

Alfie went home to do chores,
and worked really hard at staying focused.

Alfie broke bigger tasks out
into smaller ones.

Sometimes Alfie left notes in the den
to remember what to do next.

MAKE YOUR BED, ALFIE! LOVE, ALFIE

Alfie's parents noticed the changes,
and were so proud that they kept a daily journal
to support and encourage Alfie.

ALFIE'S BOOK
OF
PROGRESS

Every morning, they read the previous night's
progress so Alfie could start each
night off on a positive note.
(After all, wolves are nocturnal - silly!)

Alfie even came up with a rhyme to help
quiet both body and mind:

My focus is a muscle that I choose to flex.
When I slow down and breathe
I feel my best.

Now, Alfie still struggles with an active mind and body, but by relaxing and practicing mindfulness every day, it's a whoooole lot better.

The silver lining is that Alfie appreciates being able to get everything done and making the most out of every day.

YOUR SILVER LINING TOOLKIT
Use these tools with Alfie to help yourself slow down!

Practice mindfulness. Sit somewhere quiet and focus on your breathing and being still.

Stay physically active. A strong body means a strong mind.

Picture yourself being calm and focused in your mind.

Keep a journal of everything that you do well for positive reinforcement, or have your parent, sibling or friend keep one for you.

Break larger tasks into smaller tasks.

Leave yourself notes to remind yourself of things you need to do.

Come up with a rhyme to help you focus and slow down.

And hey, everyone can have a hard time focusing and calming down!
What do other kids do to help themselves focus and stay calm?

Noah, 8 years old
"To stay focused I stay quiet. To calm down I take deep breaths."

Sandy, 9 years old
"I go to a quiet spot to calm down."

Colin, 7 years old
"I eat something that's not sugary and relax."

Ian, 11 years old
"I go somewhere by myself to help me calm down."

Yahvi, 7 years old
"I try to relax and read my favorite book."

For Caregivers

Every child can learn from the benefits of mindfulness, relaxation, and positive reinforcement. This is especially true of children with ADHD who are hyperactive, inattentive, and impulsive.

These are certainly common traits in most children, but it's important to note when their behavior feels extreme and gets in the way of them leading productive lives. It is always best to contact a professional such as a child therapist or psychologist if this is the case, to get your child the treatment they need.

The strategies noted in this book, among many others, can help you and your child manage their behavior. These are skills that will build the foundation of life-long coping mechanisms. Spending time going over these skills together can help them learn and grow.

Communication

It's important to be open about the challenges that ADHD presents for your child and address them honestly. This can be at bedtime, over meals, or in car rides—whenever your child is comfortable. Really listen to them and give them your full attention. It's also important that they know ADHD does not define them. In fact, the challenges that it can cause can make them stronger, more resilient children in the long run.

Positive reinforcement

Pay attention to the things that they do well and note them. Create a list, like Alfie's parents do, and read it back to them. This requires you to take the time to notice their behavior frequently. It's a lot easier to notice bad behavior than good behavior. Set reminders for this if needed. When children have greater self-esteem they feel more confident to keep going in the right direction instead of acting out. Remember, no child wants to have a temper tantrum or act out. Children want to succeed. Being patient, supportive, and empathetic will help both of you.

Mindfulness

This is important for children and adults alike, and especially those with ADHD. This is simply slowing down and being present in the moment while quieting the mind. You can do this together with your child when they need to be reminded to slow down. Focus on your breathing – in through your nose and out through your mouth - while letting your racing mind slow down. You can include Alfie in this as well and do it together. They are partners in this after all!

Consistency

Life is busy and demanding, but it's so important to carve time out of your day to work on these tactics. Repeated practice is the key to achieving most things, and this is no different.

Self-Care

Last but not least, it's essential to take care of the caretaker. Carve out time for yourself to do something restorative that is just for you. It may feel counter-intuitive to take time away from your child, but it's so important to be healthy to be the best care provider you can be.

About the authors

Sara Moore is a Creative Director, living in Los Angeles. She was diagnosed with depression and anxiety at a young age and is forever grateful to her family for getting her the treatment she needed and being an unwavering source of support. She learned coping skills that she's used throughout her life and hopes every child who needs them will use those same skills found in these books. Sara founded Silver Lining Stuffies so that every child who has these same challenges knows that they are never alone. *They are stronger and braver than they know* and they now have a furry friend to whom they can relate, as well as a community of supportive, like-minded children and adults.
For more information visit **www.silverliningstuffies.com.**

Christopher Piehler is an award-winning playwright and storyteller living in West Hollywood with his wife and two cats.